Once upon a t

GW01007085

Little Red Riding Ho

Jack and the beansta... ..

Little Red Riding Hood

Once upon a time
there was a little girl and
her name was
Little Red Riding Hood.

She lived with her mother
near a big wood.

One day her mother said,
"Your granny is ill.
Take some cakes for her to eat."

Now Little Red Riding Hood's
granny lived right in the middle
of the wood.

Little Red Riding Hood set off.
She walked deeper and
deeper and deeper
into the wood.

All at once a wicked wolf
jumped out and said,
"What is your name
little girl?"

Little Red Riding Hood
told him her name because
she was frightened.

Then the wicked wolf said,
"Where are you going
Little Red Riding Hood?"

Little Red Riding Hood said,
"I am going to my granny's
with some cakes."

The wicked wolf ran
as fast as he could
to granny's house.

He knocked on the door
and granny said,
"Who's that?"

Then the wicked wolf
made his voice very soft
and said,
"It's Little Red Riding Hood."

WELCOME

Granny said,
"That's all right then,
come in."

The wicked wolf ran in
and ate granny up.
Yes, he ate every bit!

Then the wicked wolf
put on granny's night cap
and granny's glasses
and got into granny's bed.

Little Red Riding Hood
got to her granny's house.

She knocked on the door
and the wicked wolf said,
"Who's that?"

Little Red Riding Hood said,
"It's Little Red Riding Hood
and I've brought you
some cakes to eat."

The wicked wolf said
in his soft voice,
"Come in my dear."

So Little Red Riding Hood
went into granny's house.

Little Red Riding Hood
looked at her granny and said,
"Oh granny,
what big **eyes** you've got!"

"All the better to **see**
you with, my dear!"
said the wicked wolf.

Then Little Red Riding Hood
looked again and said,
"Oh granny,
what big **ears** you've got!"

"All the better to **hear**
you with, my dear!"
said the wicked wolf.

Then Little Red Riding Hood
looked once more and said,
"Oh granny,
what big **teeth** you've got!"

"All the better to **eat**
you with, my dear!"
said the wicked wolf.

Then the wicked wolf
jumped out of bed
to eat her up.

But just then a wood-cutter
heard the wicked wolf and
he ran in with his axe.

The wood-cutter took one look
at the wicked wolf.

He lifted his axe,
chopped the wicked wolf in half
and out came granny!

After that granny got back
into bed and they all
ate the cakes for tea.

So that was the end
of the wicked wolf
and this is the end
of the story.

Jack and the beanstalk

Once upon a time
there was a boy and
his name was Jack.

One day Jack's mother said,
"We are very poor.
We have no money and
we will have to sell the cow.
Take her to market, Jack."

So Jack set off
with the cow.
On the way to market
he met a little old man.

The little old man said,
"Give me the cow and
you can have some magic beans."

So Jack gave him the cow and
took the magic
beans.

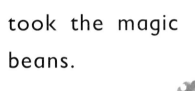

When Jack got home
his mother was very cross and said,
"I wanted money for the cow.
These beans are no good!"

She threw the magic beans
out of the window and
sent Jack to bed
without any supper!

Next morning Jack looked out
and saw a great big beanstalk
going right up into the sky.

"I want to climb that beanstalk,"
said Jack.

So Jack climbed up and up
and up and up,
right to the very top.

At the top of the beanstalk
Jack found a long road.
At the end of the long road
he saw a giant's house.

"I want to see who lives there,"
said Jack.

So Jack went to the giant's house
at the end of the long road and
he went inside.

Soon the giant came back home.

He sniffed and sniffed,

and then he shouted,

"Fe Fi Fo Fum!

I smell the blood of an Englishman.

Be he alive or be he dead

I'll grind his bones to make my bread!"

So Jack hid in the oven
and the giant sat down
with his bag of gold.

Well, the giant fell asleep.
Jack got out of the oven.
"I want that bag of gold,"
said Jack.

So he took the bag of gold
and climbed down and down
and down and down,
right to the bottom
of the beanstalk.

GOLD

Jack and his mother
were not poor now.
They bought lots of food and
a new cow with the giant's gold.

But one day Jack said, "I want to
climb that beanstalk again."

So Jack climbed up and up
and up and up,
right to the very top.

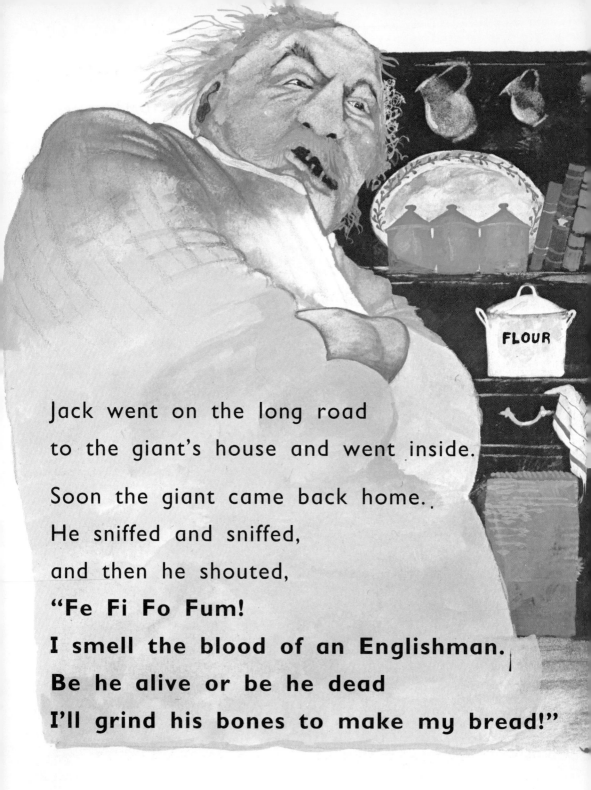

Jack went on the long road
to the giant's house and went inside.

Soon the giant came back home.
He sniffed and sniffed,
and then he shouted,
"Fe Fi Fo Fum!
I smell the blood of an Englishman.
Be he alive or be he dead
I'll grind his bones to make my bread!"

Jack hid in the oven. .
It was very hot!

The giant sat down
with his magic hen.
The giant said,
"Lay an egg."
And the magic hen
laid a **golden** egg.

Well, the giant soon fell asleep
and Jack got out of the oven.

"I want that magic hen,"
said Jack.

So he took the magic hen
and climbed down and down
and down and down,
right to the bottom
of the beanstalk.

cluck
cluck

Now Jack and his mother
were very, very, **very** rich.
The magic hen laid
golden eggs for them
and they had lots of money.

But one day Jack said,
"I want to climb the beanstalk again."

So he climbed up and up
and up and up,
right to the very top.

Jack went on the long road
to the giant's house and went inside.
The giant came back and shouted,
"Fe Fi Fo Fum!
I smell the blood of an Englishman.
Be he alive or be he dead
I'll grind his bones to make my bread!"

So Jack hid and the giant sat down.
This time he had a magic harp and
the magic harp sang to him.

Jack said,
"I want that magic harp!"
Well, the giant soon fell asleep
and Jack took the magic harp
but the harp sang out, "Help! Help!"

The giant woke and ran after Jack
all the way down the long road
to the beanstalk.

Jack climbed down and down
and down and down.
The giant climbed down and down
and down and down after him.

But Jack got an axe and
chopped down the beanstalk
and the giant was killed.

So that was the end
of the giant
and this is the end
of the story.